Pop's socks

Pop has odd socks on.
Can he fix it?

Pop gets a box of socks.
He tips the box up.

He picks up a sock.
It has a fox on it.

8

He tugs at a sock.
It has lemons on it.

Pop digs into the socks and gets red socks.

He has a duck sock
and a hen sock.

It is too hot for socks.
Pop has no socks on.

Before reading

Say the sounds: c k ck j qu v w x y z zz ff ll ss
Ensure the children use the pure sounds for the consonants without the added "uh" sound, e.g. "llll" not "luh".

Practise blending the sounds: box sock socks fox lemons duck picks hen red hot odd fix tugs gets digs tips Pop's Pop

High-frequency words: can it on up at and
Tricky words: he the into too no of is has for

Vocabulary check: Review the meaning of the verbs "tips", "tugs" and "digs". Get the children to demonstrate these actions.
odd – What does it mean when someone says "you have odd socks on"? What is the opposite to odd in this context? (matching)

Story discussion: Look at the cover illustration and read the title. What do you notice that looks a little odd? What could Pop do about his non-matching (or odd) socks?

Teaching points: Review /c/ /k/ and /ck/. Each of these graphemes represent the same sound. Explain to children that ck never comes at the beginning of a word. Create a list of ck words (sock, duck, pick, sack, rock) and draw a line under the two letters to indicate that they represent one sound. Review the use of question marks and possessive apostrophes (Pop's). Review two-syllable words (lemons).

After reading

Comprehension:
- Where does Pop keep all of his socks?
- Describe some of the socks that Pop has.
- What was wrong with the two red socks Pop found?
- Which socks did he wear in the end?

Fluency: Speed read the words again from the inside front cover.